ONE PAGE INDIAN

(A collection of Tamil sho:

Translated from Tamil
by
A.Basheer Ahmad Jamali

CONTENTS

PREFACE

While novels and long stories were written and read predominantly since the beginning of 20th century, writing short one page stories started appearing understandably since the eighties of the last century when televisions entered the Indian houses and consumed much of the daily time of the people. Today we see stiff competition among hundreds of TV channels in India to captivate the attention of the masses, who, because of which, hardly get any time to read a novel or long story. After the advent of the globalization process and the onslaught of televisions, computers, tablets, internets and smartphones, people everywhere get themselves tied with any of those devices and they hardly get time even to read. Where is the time and patience for them to read a long story or a big novel? Indians, if at all read, read mostly or only during their daily travel from their homes to offices and back. Here also only those who use public transports for their travels would do so. Otherwise, we find more and more people choosing to drive their own four wheelers and two wheelers to their workplaces and thereby losing their reading habits. Those who make long distance travel, also tend to read. We could see many of them carry periodicals- weeklies and monthlies – with them and read them during their travel on board buses and trains. These periodicals mostly, if they are in regional languages, carry very short stories, most of which could be just in one page or less than that. Hence writing such very short stories or one-page stories has become the trend nowadays and has become a genre in itself in our contemporary literature.

In this prevailing trend, the Indian writers have shown their creative skill and imaginative talent in writing one page stories in a tremendous way. Because writing one page stories, in my opinion, is much more difficult than writing a long story running into several pages. If a story is to be written in one page, the text has to be extremely attractive and enormously delightful to read. When we read one page stories in weeklies and monthlies, we realize how best the Indian writers have turned out to be in writing these stories in simple styles with easy vocabularies. They, above all, keep the outcome of the story or plot an undisclosed secret until the last paragraph or the last line or at times even the last word. This is what certainly stirs happy amazement sometimes and merry laughter at some other times.

In the light of the above, it gives me immense pleasure to present to the English readers a bouquet of 50 Indian short stories of one page each. The collection of these fifty stories were taken from among hundreds of stories that appeared in Tamil weeklies since the eighties of the 20th century up to the first decade of this century. These were first translated into Arabic and published in the year 2011 by Arabnet Publication, Calicut. When they were well received by the Arabic readers including native Arabs, I thought of translating them into English too and present them to the English readers. Hence, this collection of stories that reflect contemporary Indian culture.

The reader will find an illustrative picture beside each story suitable to the context and reflecting the lifestyles and social traditions of the Indians. I hope these pictures will please the readers and induce them to read further and further until they finish the whole book.

I avail this opportunity to express my sincere thanks to all story contributors or writers whose names appear under each story. I would also like to thank all Tamil weeklies especially Kumutham from which most stories were taken.

A. Basheer Ahmad Jamali,
Trichy- Tamil Nadu

1. KINSHIP

I had collected three-quarters of the money required for my son to get the new job. I was taxing my mind to find ways to get the rest of the money. At that moment my wife, whose other name is 'beautiful idea', said "Is there not your uncle in Tambaram? Why don't you go to him?"

My uncle had lost his wife sometime back and he had no children. After his retirement, he was living alone in a rented house in Tambaram. I visited him, as per the advice of my wife, the very next day.

"How are you, uncle?" I entered his home with this inquiry, and I sat down with him.

"I am very pleased with your visit, my son, because there are a lot of our relatives who do not care about visiting me. And I am very grateful to you for you are the only man who loves his relatives and visits them regularly" he said holding my hand with tenderness and warmth.

I sat and spoke to him for a while and returned home without telling him what I had in mind.

How glad he was with my visit and how could I have polluted his feelings about me by conveying to him my paltry demand.

(Janardhanan)

2. DAUGHTER'S HEART

"How are you Mummy?" With these words my daughter entered our house and hugged me and I held her to my chest

"I'm fine, thank God, O my soul," I exclaimed and made her sit in the hall and went to the kitchen to bring her a cup of drinking water.

She had come to my house six months after her marriage. Before her marriage she was crying when she saw her father painfully borrowing a lot of money to meet the expenses of the marriage and was also adamant that she won't marry such a man who was trying to impose a huge amount of loan on her father.

In any case, thank God that she has been married now and has started to live with her husband for the last six months.

After a moment my daughter came slowly to the kitchen behind me and called me "Hey Mummy" adding

"your son-in-law travels every day by public transport to his office and you know that there are always jams on the buses these days. My husband is suffering from extreme fatigue because of traveling for long hours and I can not stand his suffering. "Ma, I know that father has already borrowed a lot of money, but please understand my husband's condition. I want him to buy a motor-cycle for his son-in-law by borrowing a little more sum over the previous loan."

Here is my daughter crying for her husband today, the one who was crying for her father yesterday! (La-

DR A BASHEER AHMAD

lith Sellappa)

3. BETTER BY CAR

"It's time, come quickly," I called my wife as we were hurrying to attend the wedding of a friend of ours.

Minutes later, my wife stood ready in front of me in the most beautiful fashion and said: "Let's go". We went outside towards our car parked in front of the house, but she pointed to the motorbike parked beside the car for the ride. I said, "Why not by car?"

"You know, my love, the people of your friend are not rich enough and if we go by car, they might think that we are showcasing our wealth"

I told her "No, my dear, they won't think as you say. On the contrary, they will be happy with those who go to them by car as it will prove to all those present at the wedding that the groom's family also has rich friends."

She accepted my words and we went by car.

(Paramasivam)

4. CHARITY

"You were doing good to all , donated to all most of what you earned and always wished good for your friends, relatives and neighbors but what you got at the end was nothing for all your charity and good work" said wife Sadna to her husband Shekar while pouring poison into the two cups of juice.

Shekar saw his watch that showed 11:30 pm and he thought for a moment that he won't have to repay the debt from now on. When both the husband and wife brought the cups near their lips, the doorbell rang.

Shekar hid the cup and opened the door.
"How are you my brother?" So asking, embraced him Rama, the son of his father's second wife.

"Take your house documents and these gold ornaments worth three lakh rupees. This is your share which my mother had taken by deceiving our father. Excuse us, my brother, I have travelled a long distance, please allow me to stay with you in your home for the night and tomorrow I'll go to my office from here ."
Shekhar looked at his wife and smiled at the way his destiny changed his life.

(Ilangkumaran)

5. LOSS

Trader Dinesh laid the foundation stone to build a big hotel in the city. The engineer offered him an idea

"Sir, I suggest making the car parking under the building"

"But, will it not be expensive?"

"We do not need to dig the ground ourselves, Sir"

"How?"

"Let us spread the rumor that we found a treasure of gold when we dug the ground for foundation. The people from the Archaeological department will arrive and dig the whole ground. They will go back announcing that they couldn't find anything. We will thus get the ground dug up without any expenditure.

Dinesh was pleased and did as advised by the engineer.

The officials from the Department of Archaeology came, dug the ground and searched for gold but found skeletons. They declared that the ground was a cemetery thus making it a Government property and that the purchase of the plot was not permissible!

(Thenkalan)

6. MISSION FAILURE

"Take the lunch box, uncle. You left it there, where you sat." So saying the boy sighing rapidly gave the box to him.

"Thank you, my dear" said Raja.

"You need not thank me, uncle, this is my duty. I lost my box with lunch in it last week and I was hungry that day and, in the evening, when I went to my house and told my mother what had happened, my mother kept weeping and did not take her dinner that night"

"Thus, your mother may feel sad and cry if she comes to know that you lost your lunch box and did not take your lunch."

"Take your lunch, uncle" the boy went after uttering these words. Now after opening the box and disabling the bomb, Raja, the terrorist regretted the failure of his mission!

(Vishnu Kumar)

7. SHOCK

While arriving by taxi I wasn't sure if I had reached the correct street or was it the next one? So, I wanted to ask the taxi driver, but wasn't sure on how to call him because I did not see a name tag on his shirt. I was hesitant to call him by saying "Hey, driver!" because it did not sound respectable. So, I touched him on the shoulder, to draw attention to my query.

Suddenly his body shuddered and he could not control the car which started running randomly, and it almost hit the cars and pedestrians coming from the opposite direction. Fortunately, he somehow managed to stop the car along the sidewalk.

I was surprised to at the scene and looked at him confused

He said: "Don't do like this, sir,"

"Sorry, I did not expect you to be startled like this for just a simple touch on the shoulder."

"It has a reason, sir"

"What is that?"

"I started driving a taxi just today. For the last twenty-five years, I was a driver driving the vehicles in the morgue, carrying dead bodies!"

(Shekh Zinda Madar)

8. BED

My husband and I went to the furniture shop to buy a bed for our newly married daughter. The shopkeeper offered us a bigger bed but the price was very high and my husband left it and chose a smaller bed for a lesser price. I got angry and told him, "Why do you choose the small bed? Is it because of it being cheap? Didn't you hear the shop owner saying, if we purchase a bigger bed, even the children could sleep later on? We buy the bed only once, why be stingy and why not buy the larger one?"

"If the bed is large, the husband will sleep at one end and the wife at the other end and the real love and affection may not happen between them but if the bed is smaller, the couple will sleep together touching and hugging each other and thereby love will develop between them" said my husband laughingly.

(Kumar)

9. SPEECH

"I thought that there was no other woman as talkative as you but it seems that women all over the world are chatterboxes." Majid said, reading a newspaper

"Are you kidding?" his wife asked him.

"Men speak an average of 1500 words a day whereas women speak 3000 words, I do not say this, but here a research article in the newspaper says so"

"Yes, there is a reason for that, my darling," laughed Tahira and added "If men say something, we women understand and grasp it immediately but if we say something, you people do not understand easily. You guys do not understand anything unless we repeat it twice all the time. Hence we need to speak twice as much as men speak."

"What?" He said.

(Shekh Zinda Madar)

10. WHAT TO BE?

"Hey Jhano, Don't you hear me calling? What are you thinking about?"

"Sorry, I only think about the future of our son Ramesh. We have to make him a great doctor"

"Give up this thought you crazy girl! Don't you see in every street board, the names of at least four doctors? Let him study M.B.A Master of Business Administration, so that he can get a big salary"

"Let us both leave these two ideas. He should study engineering like Saraswati's husband. You see, whenever he builds something for any contractor, he builds a house for himself as well."

"This is like the story of some shops where buying a T-shirt gets you another for free. I want our son to go out of the country and earn thousands of dollars"

"We have only one son and you want to send him to America? No! Nothing! He will study law here and become a famous lawyer!"

"No study will be suitable to him. I have an idea. Listen well. This is the final one. He will study computers. According to his astro-logical figures, he would one day become Bill Gates!"

"Doesn't matter; first wake him up from bed. And see how soundly he sleeps! Without knowing what is going on between the parents about his future"

This child Ramesh who only began attending his KG classes since the previous day was fast asleep.   (Bala Vishwanathan)

11. REWARD

Supaiya, carrying a heavy canvas bag, came out of the bank amidst a great jam of customers. Placing the bag on the handlebar, he was about to start pedaling the cycle.

A man came to him saying, "Sir, look below, a one hundred rupee note has fallen from your pocket!" and when Supaiya bent down to take it the man took the bag hanging on the handle bar and ran away quickly.

People gathered around and asked him, "The man threw the paper note on the ground to divert your attention and snatched away the bag of money. Why did you get yourself deceived by him?"

The man coolly sat on his bicycle and quietly started to proceed, telling the gathering "Just today I was able to complete a task that the bank manager assigned me a week ago. The manager asked me to kill a large rat that was living in the record room causing a lot of inconvenience. I was able to kill the mouse only today, which I folded in a paper and put it in the bag to throw it away outside in a dustbin. The man thought that the cloth bag contained a lot of money.

Poor man! When he opens it, he will realize and throw the dead mouse in the garbage. He has only exempted me from that task. He has also given me Rs 100 as a reward!" So saying, he started pedaling his bicycle, speeding towards his house. (V.Lokanathan)

12. DIFFERENCE

Karim came to India during the summer holidays from New York. The next day he entered the market in Panagal Park. "Oh, look at the scorching heat here, Maliha. It's only ten o'clock in the morning! The weather would be much nicer at this time in America!" He said to his wife.

When they went out of the market proceeding towards their car they saw crowded people, motorcycles and livestock. He said: "We don't see such problems in New York. See, this is the difference between our country and the US"

After returning to New York, they went to the supermarket and after shopping there, on their way back, Karim said to his wife "We have spent $ 22 to buy vegetables for just one day. This is equivalent to Rs 1000, how expensive it is! For this amount we can buy vegetables in our country enough for a whole week. How wonderful is our country!"

(Shekh Zinda Madar)

13. FIERCELY

"What do you say, finally? Are you going to your father and re-turning back with the fifty thousand or not?" he asked furiously.

"No! this is not good" replied his wife.

He slapped her violently on the face!

The weekly quarrel between Jamuna and Venkatesh reached its peak that day.

Jamuna decided and immediately went out of her house and rushed to the police station located at the street end.

"Come in" welcomed the Police

She narrated to him all that had happened between her and her husband without sparing anything.

"Has it come to this point?!" said the policeman adding, "Doesn't matter. Go to him now and tell that I'll come to him personally with the money next week"

After listening to the words of her police father, Jamuna felt re-assured and walked back to the house of her husband wiping the tears from her eyes.

(Maha Baskaran)

14. PEN

"Idiots! They always ask for a pen. Do they go to the cinema without money? But when they come to the bank, I don't know how they forget their pens!" Thus thought Raghu and hid the pen in the inner pocket of his shirt.

An elderly man interrupted him and asked him, "O brother, will you please write this form for me?"

"I have no pen," said Raghu casually.

"I did not expect this from you. I am an illiterate person, not knowing how to read and write and so I don't need a pen. But you look like an educated man! Are you also like me? Did you go any time to the cinema without money? We are going through the worst of times! It will be no wonder if you leave your hands at your home and go out just to avoid helping people!" said the elderly man and left.

Raghu felt heavily ashamed and took the pen from inside the shirt and put it back in his front pocket.

(Uma Maheshwari)

15. SMART PROTECTION

Gomati was afraid to leave her young daughter at home, while she went out. When going out, her husband shouted loudly while bidding farewell to their daughter.

Gomati got angry at her husband' s and said, "I already told you that we should go without anyone's notice. But now all the people have come to know, especially the young boys who are playing here, that we are going out and our daughter is very much alone in our house. And I am scared of leaving her alone at home" "Do not worry... my dear. Now all these boys know that our daughter is alone in the house. All of them will be parading and circumambulating around our house until we come back in the evening and our neighbors throughout the day will be watching curiously as to what our daughter is going to do. Do you find any better protection for our daughter other than this arrangement?" asked her husband.

 Gomati now understood the smartness of her husband!

(Siva Subramanian)

16. WHO?

Shankaran requested the marriage broker Varadan to find a beautiful girl for his beloved son. Even if the girl was poor it wouldn't matter. Varadan took him to a house.

"Is not your mother in the house, Lakshmi?" Varadan asked her.

"She has gone to the temple and will return soon, please come in," said Lakshmi, switching on the fan. Shortly afterwards she offered them a cup of sweet fragrant coffee with a smile.

"While we wait for her mother's return, let me give you some information about her, Brother, Lakshmi is the only girl to her parents in this house. She has completed a Bachelor of Commerce. She has computer knowledge and knows how to respect people. She has all the required virtues but could not succeed in the dowry market," said Varadan in a sad voice.

"I like Lakshmi and I think she is a suitable bride for my son. I agree and approve of this alliance. But you seem to have much feeling for Lakshmi, why?"

Varadan replied, "I... I am the father of Lakshmi!"

(Tamil Nayahi)

17. ABSENCE

"Why didn't Ragavan attend the funeral of his wife?"

"Ten years have gone since he went abroad to work. At least now he should've come".

"Maybe he married another girl?!"

People who came to condole the women's death were wondering in this manner. All the funeral rituals got over without the presence of her husband.

Mahesh, his son, was quite angry thinking about his father.

On the second day, "Ragavan is dead and his body will reach you" came the news from abroad.

Mahesh was shocked and saddened. A few days later came a letter from his father written before his death.

"Mahesh beloved,

Greetings,

Your mother has suffered severe hardships ever since she married me. I went abroad for your welfare, our four children. She took my place to take care of you and to bring all of you up. It was when I decided to leave this work and return there to take care of you all, that I received the news of your mother's death, who lived for me and dedicated her life for the sake of my children for those ten long years. I have no desire to live after the one who lived for me and my children has died. That is why I have decided to die and meet my beloved in the hereafter. I would like to request you all four to live in this world always with love and co-operation among yourselves.With love and regards,

Ragavan.

"Daddy!" yelled Mahesh at the top of his voice weeping bitterly.

(Rajesh)

18. SAME BOAT

During a walk with his second wife in a market street, Suresh became pale as he saw a couple approaching him. Yes, no doubt, she was his first wife coming with another unknown man. "How did she come here?" he thought with concern and confusion. He wiped his sweating face with his handkerchief as he looked at his new wife with a side glance.

Her face was also in the red with fear; as if a jinn or a ghost had struck her. "How does she know about my past wife?" thought Suresh.

"What happened to you, Nandini, you look perplexed?" he asked her. In the meantime, the couple crossed them over and went into a shop inside the market. "Thank God," his heart got relieved and then he asked his wife again, "Why do you look perplexed?"

She replied, "Did you see the couple who just crossed us? The man was my ex-husband. I got him divorced and married you afterwards."

Suresh was wondering whether to laugh or weep!

(S. Kamala)

19. BLACK AND WHITE

"Why are the people standing there with white colour flags in their hands? Do they mean peace?" I asked him

He said, "Usually, some dimness strikes people's eyes but in your case a watermelon seems to have blocked your eyes"

"Why?"

"Why not? People here are waving black flags, man, they are protesting against the visiting minister. When are you going to wear glasses?"

"Yes, there is a bug in my eyes and I am unable to see things well ,these days."

I decided to go to a good eye specialist and finally I had an appointment with one.

"Doctor, I have a problem in my eyes, I do not have proper vision and I see black as white, Doctor, will you please examine my eyes?"

"Without a doubt, my brother, because you do not differentiate between black and white coats! I am wearing a black coat because I am a lawyer, please go to a doctor."

"What??????????"!

(Damo)

20. DONKEY

Rashid, the washerman, was rearing a donkey for several years and one day the donkey in a fit of anger kicked him strongly. His health deteriorated and he died some days later.

Many men and women came from among his relatives and friends to his house to offer condolences. The men sat with his brothers, and women with his widowed wife, to offer condolence. A woman was watching from a distance Rashid's wife talking to the women sitting with her and saw them asking her for something which she declined. The woman wanted to know what was going on.

After all the mourners left the house, the woman went to the widow and asked her "What were you strongly refusing to do to the women who came for condolence?" The widow said, "Because they wanted to buy the donkey from me!"

(Sheik Zinda Madar)

21. SCHOOL SWEETNESS

"What is the point in sending Samad to school? He does not want to attend the school and study there," said his mother, Halima, to her husband.

Rahman called his son who was seven years old and asked him to bring a basket of coal. He brought a basket of coal. Now the father asked his son to empty the coal from the basket and fetch a basket of water from the stream running behind their house.

Abdul Samad did what his father told. He went with the empty basket to the stream and tried to take water and bring it to his father, but no water remained in the basket and all of it drained away from the pores. When he reached his father, the basket was empty.

His father said, "Go again, my son, and take the water and come here quickly," His son did accordingly, but the basket came back empty without a drop of water.

And now, the father asked his son to look into the basket which became pure and clean

Son said "Dad, what a clean basket! How beautiful it is!"

The father said to his son, "Did you see, the basket has become clean and pure even if no water is left there in the basket. This is how your going to school will also be. God willing, you will become a clean and virtuous man if you get a good education and that does not mean just passing in the exams!"

(Sheik Zinda Madar)

22. DOUBT

Suman couldn't believe that his wife, Nila had changed completely.

Since the arrival of the new Director, Suman noticed a change in the behavior of his wife. Earlier she used to return home from her office at six o'clock in the evening, but these days she was late and sometimes she even came in the manager's car. He could not tolerate this and was in a big rage.

After a few days he told her, "Nila, you are always talking about your manager and keep praising him a lot; you also come home very late. This is unacceptable, and from tomorrow I will not allow you to go to your office."

"No, darling, mine is a very good manager, and six months ago her husband died. She is new to the town. I help her to alleviate her suffering and sit with her for some time, talking to her so that she can get some consolation and. Is this wrong?"

When Suman understood that his wife's manager was a woman, he was ashamed of himself and never doubted his wife again.

"I'm very sorry, my dear Nila!"

(Accha)

23. HOPE

Her car broke down, so Savitry took a taxi. Before boarding, she read what was written on the back of it "Pregnant women will be carried to the hospital for free," and while traveling she asked the taxi driver Govindan, "How many pregnant women have you so far carried to the hospital?"

"At least 20, Madam," replied Govindan

"Has your wife traveled by your taxi?"

"Yes, once every day, because she believes and hopes that if she sits where pregnant women have sat, she too would one day become pregnant" he answered with a mixed sense of hope and disappointment.

Savitri stopped the taxi in front of a maternity hospital and before getting down she gave Govindan her visiting card and said "You are doing the community a great service. Come to me with your wife. I take the responsibility for free treatment for both of you until a child is born.

At that moment, Savitri, the famous doctor of obstetrics and gynecology, appeared to Govindan as a divine gift from heaven!

(Kumar)

24. REASON

"Our neighbour Yassin has seen you every day coming out of the orphanage located at the end of our Alley and has told his wife about it. She asked me yesterday wondering what you were doing at the orphanage.",'did he leave any of his children there?' "

Ever since this woman asked me in that fashion, I am quite sad. Tell me the truth now" his wife said with great gloom and concern.

   Perumal said "As you know that the poor and middle class travel by the bus where I work as a conductor. Very often, I am not able to pay the remaining money after giving them a ticket. So I go to the orphanage every day to give them what is left after calculating the whole transaction, praying that the reward of such a gift to an orphanage should reach them"

   Wife Padma took the hand of her husband and kissed it warmly thanking God for the great charitable work of her husband.

(S. Raman)

25. POISON GAS

At 11.30 AM on Dec. 2nd the doorbell rang in one of the houses of the Chikako city.

"Yes, come in"

In came a person slowly, limping.

"Sir, I have come to spray pesticides gas"

"Ok, get to it then"

And when the stranger came closer to him, he closed his mouth and said to the resident while spraying the poisonous gas into his nose, "Don't be afraid, because you will not die, just that you can't speak and won't be able to move your feet and hands. So you will not be able to complain about me to the police.

I just want you to remember the crime you committed and regret and repent over it. Didn't you think of this day that year?"

He picked up the phone and dialed 911 and said, "Send an ambulance immediately," and quickly left the scene limping back.

On the fifth of December the stranger stood at the shrines of his wife and daughter in Bhopal and sighing deeply said to them, "He was able to obtain freedom for lack of evidence and witness in court, but the same kind of gas that ended your life has paralyzed him forever and he is now alone and suffering. Now your souls may rest in peace... I have given him what he deserves"

(R. Saradi)

26. ADVICE

At the cash counter for payments of electricity bills,
"Why are you sad, Sundaram?" - asked Selvam
"When I was calculating in the morning, I collected by mistake 100 rupees extra from a man and he was shouting at me"
"And why do you worry about it. Does he pay you or me? He is only paying to the Government and the State. Don't bother yourself. Just carry on with your work," so saying he went away.
In the evening, Selvam was traveling in the city bus and he gave the bus conductor a five rupee note and received from him a ticket for Rs 4.50 along with the remaining fifty paisa.
"Hey! Why did you give me a ticket for Rs 4.50? It's only four rupees to Saidapet"
The conductor said: "Excuse me, sir; I cut out the ticket by mistake. Please bear with me… its only 50 paisa"
"What? Is it only 50 paisa? Is this paltry sum? Give me the remainder 50 paisa. It is my money …"
Thus, continued the altercation between them, until the bus arrived at Saidapet.

(S. Sikandar)

27. WARNING

"It has been a month since I asked you to vacate the house. When do you intend to vacate? We will not be able to clean the house and live in it, unless you leave it!"

The owner of the house started shouting in this way at the tenant Muthusamy and his wife Mangalam.

"Sir, wait for just two weeks and we will vacate the house certainly by then," said the husband

"Let this be my last warning," said the house owner in a disgustful tone and went away.

His wife asked him "Why do you ask for that much period? We have already rented a new house and we can leave this house even tomorrow"

"The deadline is not for us, Mangalam. Look there at the nest built by the sparrow above the window. A new fledgling only arrived yesterday. The little bird will need a period of at least two weeks to be able to fly. If we vacate the house now, the workers who come to clean the house will throw the nest away. Think of the condition of the little one if they do so!"

(Selvaraja)

28. DISGUISE

Rajan attended the annual day function of the school where his daughter was studying. Rajan did not drink alcohol that day because his daughter was to be acting in a play organized by the school. Otherwise he was a regular drunkard.

The play started and after a short while the man got furious over his daughter as she was in the guise of a man who drank alcohol and represented her father in particular. Who wouldn't get angry at that?

But he listened to the words of some people who were sitting behind him

"See! The daughter of Rajan, What a wonderful representation in the role of a drunkard! As if she has actually drunk!" said one.

The second said "Why will she not act that way? She is after all, seeing her father, who comes home after drinking alcohol to the fullness of his stomach and seeing how much yelling and shouting he does. This might have seriously affected his young daughter. And now we are able to understand in her representation the agony she has experienced. Her father should give up drinking after seeing this drama for the sake of her future".

Rajan bowed his head in deep shame.

(Raghupati)

29. PAY RISE

Narasimhan was bouncing between heaven and earth. "How mean are you! Got an increment in your salary but didn't even bother to tell me! How arrogant and proud you are of your earnings!"

Poor Banu started crying bitterly and said with a throbbing tone "You know that my salary was less than your salary by about five hundred rupees. If my salary remained the same, no problem would have occurred. But after I got my increment six months ago, my salary has become more than yours by one thousand and two hundred rupees. If you had learned this fact you would have been upset. This is why I hid the matter from you. But look, I have opened an account in the bank in your name and have deposited all the increments since the first one in that account"

Touched by her word and deed Narasimhan reached out to his wife asking for her excuse while she opened her purse and took the passbook of the new account and put it in his hand!

(Michel Dinakaran)

30. DELIGHT

Today was the forty-second day. Sumathi was overflowing with joy. It never exceeded 30 days. Rarely was it a day or two more. This was the end result of her following many of the tips given by her mother and her mother-in-law, her neighbors and friends in addition to what she herself collected by way of information on the subject.

"I must tell this happy news to my husband, Jahan." Sumathi thought so, because it was he, who used to criticize her every time for not taking enough precaution. He also used to advise her to be more careful in future.

"This time my husband will be very happy. After many, many attempts has this happened" With this in mind, she was waiting for her husband.

She told him the news at the door itself even before he entered the house. There was no limit to her happiness.

"It has extended for twelve more days - more than ever before! If we continue like this we will reduce our expenses on the gas" said Sumathi with great joy after saving the gas fuel for the month as the couple had been suffering a lot, unable to manage their low income budget every month with their three grown-up children.

(Rama Lakshmi)

31. THE NEW SARI

Vasundra is the woman, who having lost her husband, is spending her whole life in the upbringing of her only son, Vinod and thereby trying to forget about the loss of her husband.

One day she came home early from office. As she was cleaning the house, she went to her son's room for the same. There she saw a new Sari in a small carton box. She got confused thinking "Why has he bought this sari? Has he fallen in love with any girl?" She thought of asking him as soon as he came back. Vinod came back as usual at ten and without taking his dinner he told his mother "I have to read a lot, Mom, don't disturb me" so saying he closed the door of his room immediately. She got very angry as she could not speak to him, but she concealed her anger and decided to ask him the next morning. She could not know when sleep overcame her because after a while, she slept off.

In the early morning of the next day, her son Vinod woke her up saying, "Wake up, ma, happy birthday to you!" After she heard her son's voice in the early morning, Vasundra opened her eyes and saw in his hands the same sari that she had seen in his room the day before. She was filled with joy and delight with that precious gift from her beloved son.

(Buvana)

32. POSITIVE POINT

A man was running a grocery shop in a small village. His shop became famous in the village as people often came to his shop to purchase whatever they wanted. His son who was studying in the city returned one day to his village for the holiday. He told his father "Dad, I read in the newspaper that the country this year is going to suffer because of the economic crisis and slow down and people will not have enough money" The illiterate merchant who listened to the words of his educated son believed in whatever he said. His son added saying, "Don't store and hoard much stuff and materials, dad, because people will not be able to buy them and your business will suffer a huge loss." The father who trusted his son followed his advice and did not store much in his shop. Since the shop decreased in its supplies, the number of people who used to visit his shop also reduced as they went to other shops to buy their goods. The father did not understand this and he thought that what his son said became true and that people did not have enough money because of which they did not visit his shop. He took pride in his son's knowledge and insight. As a result, his shop was the only one that suffered a huge loss that year.

(Ranjan)

33. BRIDEGROOM

Maduram went with her parents to see the bride for her younger brother. She liked the bride and agreed on the choice for her brother. The groom's father spoke to the bride's family very frankly and at the same time strongly.

"Fifty sovereigns (400 grams) of gold jewelry and six kilos of silver utensils, all necessary household items, a motorcycle for coming Deepawali and a small air-conditioner for Pongal festival. These are the very small and simple things that we expect from you. Think about it."

Maduram after seeing the bride went to her husband and returned to her father the next day. She said, "Dad, my husband is angry and he asked me whether he was anything less than my brother Murali in education or job or salary or in looks. When they chose me for him and when they said that they won't need anything in the form of dowry, you were very much pleased and smiled so wide that all your thirty-two teeth appeared. Now he says that he won't attend the wedding of my brother unless you give him a new car. He also won't send me to the wedding of my brother!"

"If the son-in-law is angry up to this point, let us not ask for anything for Murali from the house of the bride and I will tell this to them immediately." said her father.

Murali's wedding with Kalyani got over in the best way.

"My sister is the main reason for the success of our wedding," said Murali to Kalyani.

"I know, I heard that your sister's husband asked for a car" Kalyani said.

"Nothing like that happened. It was just a play enacted by my sister," said Murali to Kalyani whose eyes were filled with tears of joy.

(Annam)

34. NIGHT DUTY

Nandakumar was quite cheerful. After two weeks of request his company had accepted and turned his night duty into day duty . He was a security guard there. He had married sometime back. His wife was a policewoman and whenever he returned home after working all night, his wife was getting ready to go to the police station for her day duty. He lived in a joint family and rarely found time to be with her in private.

Nandakumar breathed a sigh of relief for he was going to work during day time from tomorrow onwards. All his nights would be spent with his wife. With all energy and vigour, he reached home. There at home, he saw his wife wearing the *khaki* dress and getting herself ready to go to office. She received him with a smile. When he tried to tell her about the change of his duty time, her sweet voice interrupted him, saying

"Be a little more patient, my darling, from tomorrow I too will have night duty and be with you during daytime. We will go to office and together come back home. Are you happy now?"

Nandakumar beat his forehead in frustration!

(Anjeyan)

35. YOU, CRAZY LADY!

"Good morning sir, I am Ragavan and I have a good job. Your daughter Usha loves me and I love her and if you accept. I'll get to marry her... and" before he could complete what he wanted to say, Usha's father Uma Shankaran interrupted saying firmly,

"Mr. Ragavan, I will give my daughter only to a senior government official".
Ragavan left the house deciding decisively to accomplish his intention.
"O father of Usha...." Kamalam, his wife, wanted to speak something.
"Shush"
Usha ran to her room crying.
After fifteen days,
The wedding of Ragavan with Uma took place nicely.
Shankaran did not attend the wedding of his daughter.
A boy, who works at the nearby video parlor, gave the video tape of their wedding to Shankaran who watched it on television.
Kamalam came and asked him, "The boy looks good and has a good job also. Why did you deny our daughter to him?"
"Hey crazy lady, do you think I did not like him? No, if I had accepted, I would have had to pay all the expenses which could not be less than hundred and fifty thousand rupees. Do we have the capacity to spend that much money? That is why I pretended to be dismissive of the marriage and now the wedding has happened at his expense, praise be to God!"
Kamalam was blown away by the smartness of her husband!
(Thamil Nayaki)

36. INDEPENDENT HOUSE

"Six months have passed since you got married. For how long will you suffer the difficulty of shared living with us? Ask your husband to look for an independent home" This is what the mother-in-law of Uma, Kalyani, told her many times.
But Uma didn't have other plans.

"Why don't you go with your husband to live independently as your mother-in-law advises you?" Vimala, her friend, asked her.

"My mother-in-law wants to send us out and give all her gold jewelry to her daughter. This is her plan. I'm not foolish enough to go out from here" replied Uma.

"We have only one son and one daughter. Our daughter is living away in her village with her husband. Why do you want to send our son and daughter-in-law from here?" Kalyani's husband Kailasam asked her with great amazement.

"Am I foolish?" Kalyani explaining her mind told her husband. "If only I say this to her, she will think that I have some tricks in mind and will decide not to go out from here. I have already disposed off all my jewelry and given it to my daughter when she got married. She doesn't know that I am wearing only imitation jewelry!"

(S. Raman)

37. WRONG CALCULATION

"Uma!", Dinesh called his wife and said, "Uma, Give the ironing cart-man 24 rupees for ironing twelve shirts"
"But we gave him 14 shirts and we have to pay him 28 rupees why do you want to give him 24 rupees only?" his wife asked him.

"Yes, Uma, I always do only like this. Does he count the shirts we give him? No. That's why I usually give him money for one or two less than the actual number"

Uma suddenly shouted, "Listen dear, we gave him 14 shirts, but he has returned back only 12. We have given him money also for only twelve shirts. And what do we do now?"
When he heard the words of Uma, Dinesh looked stunned as if he was stung by a scorpion!

(K. Arunachalam)

38. THE BETTER ONE

Kumar was sweeping the street when he saw the new teacher coming to the village. He withdrew himself and stood on the sidelines of the street. The new teacher Sukumar asked him, "Why are you trying to hide away from me, Kumar?"

"The fact of the matter is that we both were studying together in school and since you were rich and smart, you were able to complete higher education and become a teacher. But I sweep and clean the village because I was poor and dull," said Kumar, somewhat ashamed.

"No, Kumar, you sweep the streets of the village and make it clean, and I sweep the hearts of students. I get angry quickly at a student if he commits a mistake, but you do not get angry at anyone who throws garbage in the streets. You coolly come the next day and sweep the place without getting angry at anyone. Hence you are far better than me"

On hearing these words from Sukumar, Kumar raised his head and looked at him quite pleased!

(Selvaraja)

39. POVERTY

The following dialogue took place when Mari and Kari were taking tea at the local tea shop.

Mari: "Look, Kari, at my condition. I am compelled to pay medical expenses of my parents and wife with my meager salary, but I bear them with all hardship"

Kari after drinking tea left the empty cup on the table and went away silently.

"Hay, Mari, why do you say all your family problems to Kari?" asked Arumuham who came just then to take tea.

"Yes, Kari - the poor man, was complaining with sadness that his family members one after the other were suffering from diseases and his salary was not even enough to meet their medical expenses and that is why I related to Kari the problems of my family with some exaggeration, so that he would feel that his problems were less than that of mine"

"Yes, that's true, how excellent you are!" his friend, Arumuham said, praising.

(Dinesh)

40. WAGE

Toplan was walking in the street with a grass cutter on his shoulder

I called him and said "Toplan, I'll give you fifty rupees if you clean and set right my garden".

"If you give me hundred rupees I shall do what you ask me to do" Toplan said.

"No problem, I'll give you the amount you ask for" I accepted his request and he began his work in my garden.

But shortly afterwards I heard a screaming sound from the garden. When I went out there, I saw Toplan crying because a scorpion had stung him.

I took him to the hospital and got his treatment done at my expense. When he was about to go, I took a hundred rupees note from my pocket and gave it to him saying "Take your money and I will see another man tomorrow to work in my garden"

"No, sir, I didn't understand your kind self. I'll come to your house tomorrow to complete the work and take only fifty rupees from you" he said refusing to take any money from me. I looked at him surprised!

(Selvaraja)

41. PINNACLE OF POWER

Kumar came to Madurai to join his new high-grade government job as Director of the Department of Revenues. He was a successful man because he had completed his master's degree and had earned a government job as well.

He was happy and proud that he would enjoy a government position of authority.

He felt hungry on the way and entered a restaurant. There he ordered the waiter to bring him Dosa and Idli (both are eatables made from rice flour) and was waiting for the food to arrive.

The waiter came and served him Idli first and then took some time to bring Dosa. Kumar got impatient and complained to the man sitting at the cash counter about the delay as a misconduct of the waiter. But the cashier said "Sir, the man who served you with Idli and Dosa is my boss and is the owner of this shop. He asked me to sit at the cash counter as I have better knowledge of accountancy."

He then realized the greatness of the employer. His pride and arrogance disappeared instantly making him aware that in human service lies the pinnacle of power and authority.

(Arokiasamy)

42. THE CHILD LEGACY

More than ten years had passed since Kumar married Mala and they were still not blessed with a child. So they decided to adopt a child and accordingly went to an orphanage to place their request.

The management of house said "we can give you a child only after examining your home environment thoroughly"

It seemed that the process would take a month or two before they would be able to get a child.

Mala did not have the patience as her heart was always beating for a child.

"Why do you want to adopt a child only from this house? Why don't we go to another house?" Mala questioned her husband, who insisted on taking a child only from that particular orphanage.

Kumar replied "Because, Mala, this is the house from where my father and mother picked me up, thirty-five years back!"

(Subakar)

43. APPLE SMARTNESS

After we finished shopping we went down - my husband and I, to the street, and saw a line of carts where boys were selling apples.

"My apple is like honey, sir, take from me two or three kilos" said one of them.

Another boy shouted, "Look sir, these apples are from Kashmir so delicious like ice-cream"

We crossed all the carts until we got to the last one and heard the boy saying

"Sir, if you buy and eat my apple, you will feel that you have really eaten apples"

My husband stood up to him and bought from him one kilo of apples.

On the way he told me "If apples are like honey and ice-cream why should we buy apples, will not honey and ice cream do? Those boys were exaggerating"

"This is the boy who told the truth because we buy and eat apples because of their taste. We are not to taste honey and ice cream". Is my husband not smart?

(Bupadhi)

44. EID GIFT

Ahmed's colleagues were laughing at him and teased him for admitting his mistake in front of the employer whereas the mistake was committed by the manager himself, who did not register his leave application for five days. They asked him: "Why did you admit your folly when the company owner said that you did not inform the company before taking leave? Ahmed said to them,
"I told him but he did not believe me and he has cut the salary of my five days' work, doesn't matter"

His colleagues said to him, "You are a ridiculous fellow! Why should you lose your salary because of the mistake of the manager?"

In the meanwhile, the office assistant came to Ahmad and told him that the owner had called him. He went to him somewhat puzzled.

The owner told him "When I inquired about your leave, I found out that it was the mistake of the manager who has not properly marked your sanctioned leave in the record book. But you accepted the error of the manager as yours in order not to disobey me! I'm impressed and have decided to give you this gift for your Eid" and gave him a small yellow cover. Ahmad thanked him and he opened the envelope outside his office and found it containing five thousand rupees, a month's salary indeed!

(Ganesh)

45. THINK DIFFERENT

Upon getting in, I found my house unusually quiet.

It was my sister who spoke to me first; "When I was with my friend, she saw you passing by on your motorbike and said to me, referring to you, that you love her. She doesn't know that you're my brother. Is she telling the truth? Do you love her?"

She asked me quite bluntly and the room went into deep silence. All eyes were fixed on me.

I denied in an angry tone "Did your girlfriend tell you who I am and what my name is and what I do? Take the answers to these questions from her first and then come to me to talk about the matter."

In the following evening

"Excuse me, brother, she revealed her lover's name, his hometown and his job, nothing fits your description" said my sister feeling quite sorry.

I said to myself "Thank God, I had luckily told my love, changing my name given by my parents and the nature of job God had bestowed upon me. Now the matter has become manageable for me to convince my parents in due course!"

(Albert)

46. GIFT OF LOVE

One day, Sundar's sister came to his wife and told her: "Sister-in-law, I bought for you earrings and nose rings when I went on a trip to Kerala"

Sundar's wife said to her "Don't you know that these are all available here in plenty. Why should you trouble yourself to buy them in Kerala?" Her husband heard this but did not utter a word. Some days passed.

On another day, the brother of his wife came home saying to him: "Uncle, please accept these music CDs that I bought in Singapore when I traveled there on a mission" Sundar took from him the music CDs.

His wife, on seeing this, said, "These are all available here also. Why should you buy these from Singapore?"

There upon, Sundar said to her "When they were happy, they wanted to make us also happy. That is why they purchased what we like most. Don't criticize them. Don't look at what materials they give us but look at their hearts".

(Josef)

47. REJECT AND ACCEPT

Mala was surprised at the action of her husband Bala.

When her brother offered to take her family along with his family on a trip in summer vacation to Ooty at her brother's own expenses, her husband declined the offer.

When her sister's husband offered to take her to temples in the North along with his family after the annual examination, her husband declined that as well.

She was amazed when he decided to accept what her father offered.

She asked him about this and he replied. "My dear Mala, we can travel to Ooty or any religious sites in the north at any time, but the education of our son and daughter can not wait. That is why when your father, after coming to know of our economic situation, offered to bear the expenses of our children's education I accepted the offer. This is related to the future of our children. If we care about our vain dignity and refuse the offer, we will deprive our children of good education and the future will not forgive us."

Mala felt pleased and proud of her husband.

(Bartasarathi)

48. THEFT

Shiva saw the traffic police from afar. They were checking the passing cars and motorcycles. He did not have his driving license nor his helmet. When he was in fear, a policeman pointed at him to stop his bike on the roadside.

"Where do you come from?" the officer asked

"Sir, my baby has fever ...."

"Where is the license?"

"Sorry, I forgot when I rushed to buy medicine ....."

"Are you speaking the truth"

"Yes sir, by God sir,"

Freed from there, he breathed a sigh of relief. He drove his motor-cycle fast until he reached a mobile phone shop which he had fixed yesterday itself. He stopped the bike in front of the shop and walked behind it and started boring the wall. The police squad charged by the Commissioner to take necessary measures to prevent theft in Mobile shops was waiting for him inside the shop.

(Gunaseharan)

49. RIGHT TO SAY "NO"

A poor man one day knocked at the door of a house. When a lady opened the door, he asked for some alms. "There is nothing to give you," said the woman, adding "Go away from here!"

The mother-in-law of this married woman heard her words and got angry for her refusal to give charity to the poor without her permission,

"Who are you to refuse charity to this man while I'm the lady of the house?!"

The young lady immediately withdrew herself to her room sobbing.

"Thank you, madam, you are a kind and merciful lady," said the beggar ingratiatingly and added,

"All I asked from her was some paisa with which I could buy something to eat and I did not know that she was not the lady of the house"

"She is not!" interrupted the women and said "She does not have the right to refuse alms. I'm in charge here, and all the rights are with me alone and now let me tell you: We don't have anything to give you and so go away from here!"

She then shut the door on the face of the beggar!

(Folklore)

50. JAT AND THE WATERMELON

 A Jat farmer grew watermelons in his garden. One of the fruits turned out to be the largest watermelon that was ever seen in that region, and the Jat was very proud of it. People started visiting the garden and were very pleased to have a look at the impressive melon.

The king of the region one day walked down the village disguised, and arrived at the house where the Jat was living and saw the huge watermelon in his garden. Quite impressed, the King asked the Jat.

"Will you give it to me?"

"No," said the man.

"Will you sell it to me?" The King asked.

"No," the Jat said.

"What will you do with it?" the King asked.

"I intend to go to the palace and offer it to the King"

The king said, "OK, but what if the king refuses to accept that?"

"Well, then let him go to hell!" the Jat said disapprovingly.

Two days later, the Jat came to the palace with the melon and saw the King. He realized that he was the one who visited his house two days ago asking for the water melon. But he did not show that he had recognized the king.

The Jat said humbly, "I have come with a watermelon for you, Your Majesty"

The King replied, "This is very kind of you!" And added "But supposing I refuse to accept it?"

The Jat said bashfully, "You know my answer, Your Majesty!"

(Folklore)

Printed in Great Britain
by Amazon